© 2012 Age of Learning, Inc.
Published by Age of Learning, Inc., P.O. Box 10458, Glendale, California 91209.
No part of this work may be reproduced in whole or in part, or stored in a retrieval system,
or transmitted in any form or by any means, electronic, mechanical, photocopying,
recording, or otherwise, without written permission of the publisher.
ABCmouse.com and associated logos are trademarks and/or
registered trademarks of Age of Learning, Inc.

Library of Congress Cataloging-in-Publication Data
The Big Sip/Age of Learning, Inc.
Summary: In this Word Family Beginning Reader, a boy and his cat
enjoy some milk, each in his own way.

ISBN: 978-1-62116-014-4
Library of Congress Control Number: 2012912293

21 20 19 18 17 16 15 14 13 12   1 2 3 4 5
Printed in the U.S.A, on 10% recycled paper. ♻
First printing, November 2012

The Big Sip

Age of Learning, Inc., Glendale, California
This book is also available at **ABCmouse.com**, the award-winning early learning online curriculum.
Find free apps at **ABCmouse.com/apps**.

Bob likes milk.
He takes a sip.

Now the milk
is on his lip!

Bob wants more.
He takes a sip.

There is more
milk on his lip!

The cup of milk
begins to tip.
Now the milk
begins to drip!

Bob has a cat.
His name is Pip.

Bob tells Pip,
"Take a big sip!"

Drip! Drip! Drip!

Sip! Sip! Sip!

Bob sees Pip
sip up the drip.

No more milk.

No more drip.

Pip has no more
milk to sip!

To the fridge
Bob takes a trip.

Now Pip will have
more milk to sip!

The End